the source

arrangements for worship groups

book 4

B♭ instruments

arranged by Chris Mitchell

Kevin Mayhew

We hope you enjoy the music in this book.
Further copies of this and the other books in the series are available
from your local music shop or Christian bookshop.

In case of difficulty, please contact the publisher direct:

The Sales Department
KEVIN MAYHEW LTD
Rattlesden
Bury St Edmunds
Suffolk IP30 0SZ

Phone 01449 737978
Fax 01449 737834
E-mail info@kevinmayhewltd.com

Please ask for our complete catalogue of outstanding Church Music.

First published in Great Britain in 1998 by Kevin Mayhew Ltd.

© Copyright 1998 Kevin Mayhew Ltd.

ISBN 1 84003 131 X
ISMN M 57004 214 2
Catalogue No: 1470310
0 1 2 3 4 5 6 7 8 9

Cover designed by Jaquetta Sergeant

Music arrangements by Chris Mitchell

Music setting by Chris Mitchell and Lynwen Davies

Printed and bound in Great Britain by
Caligraving Limited Thetford Norfolk

Contents

This index gives the first line of each hymn. If a hymn is known by an alternative title, this is also given, but indented and in italics.

CHRIS MITCHELL is a well-established arranger, composer, musical director and session musician who has worked with Graham Kendrick, David Peacock, Gloria Gaynor and the BBC. He and his wife, Linda, are experienced worship leaders and are involved in providing seminars and workshops for Christians in the arts.

the source will be developed into a major resource for the churches. It is already available in the following editions

Words Only	ISBN	1 84003 121 2
	Catalogue No.	1470101
Full Music	ISBN	1 84003 120 4
	ISMN	M 57004 204 3
	Catalogue No.	1470104
Complete Acetate Masters	ISBN	1 84003 119 0
	Catalogue No.	1470201

Arrangements for Worship Groups:

Book 1 for C instruments	ISBN	1 84003 122 0
	ISMN	M 57004 205 0
	Catalogue No.	1470301
Book 1 for B♭ instruments	ISBN	1 84003 128 X
	ISMN	M 57004 211 1
	Catalogue No.	1470307
Book 2 for C instruments	ISBN	1 84003 123 9
	ISMN	M 57004 206 7
	Catalogue No.	1470302
Book 2 for B♭ instruments	ISBN	1 84003 129 8
	ISMN	M 57004 212 8
	Catalogue No.	1470308
Book 3 for C instruments	ISBN	1 84003 124 7
	ISMN	M 57004 207 4
	Catalogue No.	1470303
Book 3 for B♭ instruments	ISBN	1 84003 130 1
	ISMN	M 57004 213 5
	Catalogue No.	1470309
Book 4 for C instruments	ISBN	1 84003 125 5
	ISMN	M 57004 208 1
	Catalogue No.	1470304
Book 4 for B♭ instruments	ISBN	1 84003 131 X
	ISMN	M 57004 214 2
	Catalogue No.	1470310

301 Jesus, what a beautiful name

Tanya Richards

3 verses

302 Jesus, you're my firm foundation
(Firm Foundation)

Nancy Gordon and Jamie Harvill

2 verses

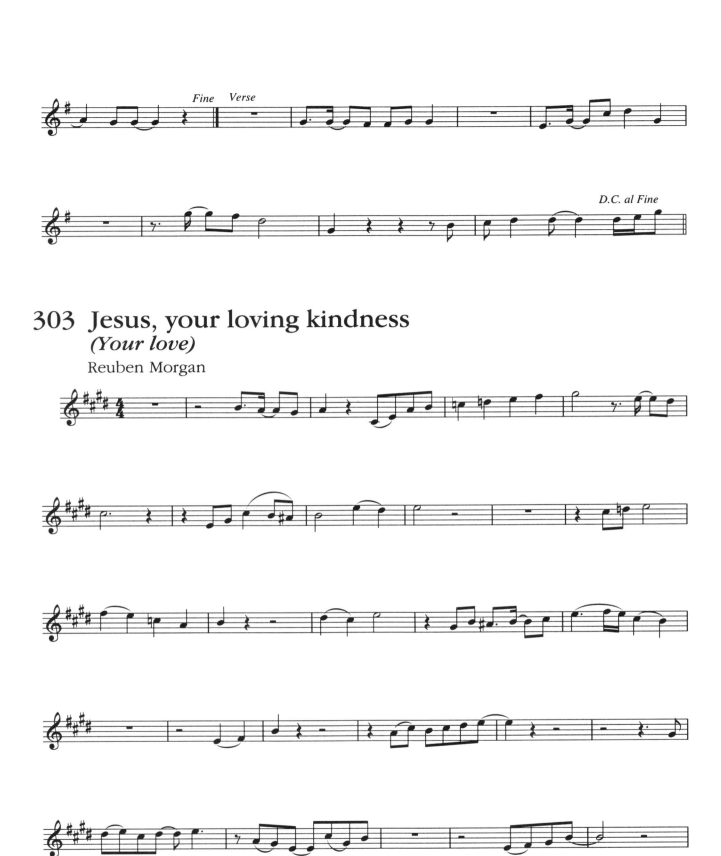

303 Jesus, your loving kindness
(Your love)

Reuben Morgan

304 Jesus, your name is power

Morris Chapman

4 verses

Freely, with feeling

305 Joy to the world

George Frideric Handel

3 verses

306 Just as I am, without one plea (Tune 1)

Henry Smart

6 verses

306a Just as I am, without one plea (Tune 2)

Arthur Henry Brown

6 verses

307 King of kings and Lord of lords

Naomi Batya and Sophie Conty

May be sung as a 2-part round

308 King of kings
(The King of glory comes)

Graham Kendrick

Strongly

309 King of kings, majesty

Jarrod Cooper

2 verses

310 Lamb of God

Chris Bowater

311 Lead us, heavenly Father, lead us

Friedrich Filitz

3 verses

312 Led like a lamb
(You're alive)

3 verses

Graham Kendrick

313 Let it be to me

Graham Kendrick

314 Let it rain

Joel Pott

315 Let me be a sacrifice

Daniel Gardner

316 Let the righteous sing

Bryn Haworth   2 verses

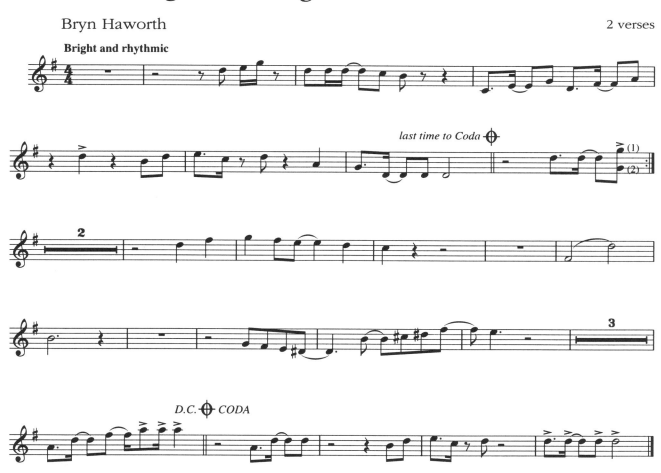

317 Let there be love

Dave Bilbrough

Triumphantly

318 Let your living water flow
(Living water)

John Watson

4 verses

With a strong beat

319 Let your love come down

Noel and Tricia Richards

2 verses

Driving

320 Let your word go forth

Robin Mark

2 verses

321 Lift up your heads
(O you gates)

Graham Kendrick

3 verses

322 Like a candle flame
(The candle song)

Graham Kendrick

3 verses

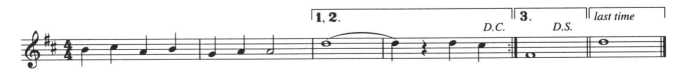

323 Living under the shadow of his wing

David Hadden and Bob Silvester

3 verses

With strength

324 Lo, he comes with clouds descending

From John Wesley's *Select Hymns with Tunes Annext*

4 verses

325 Look what God has done
(And his love goes on and on)

Graham Kendrick

3 verses

326 Look what the Lord has done

Mark David Hanby

327 Lord, for the years
(Lord of the years)

Michael Baughen

5 verses

328 Lord, have mercy
(Prayer song)

Graham Kendrick

Steadily

329 Lord, I come to you
(Power of your love)

Geoff Bullock

3 verses

330 Lord, I lift your name on high
(You came from heaven to earth)

Rick Founds

331 Lord, my heart cries out
(Glory to the King)

Darlene Zschech

332 Lord of lords

Jessy Dixon, Randy Scruggs and John Thompson

2 verses

Joyfully

333 Lord of the heavens

Lucy Fisher

334 Lord, prepare me
(Sanctuary)

John Thompson and Randy Scruggs

335 Lord, the light of your love
(Shine, Jesus, shine)

Graham Kendrick

3 verses

Majestic and steady

336 Lord, we lift you high

Judy Bailey

337 Lord, we long for you
(Heal our nation)

Trish Morgan, Ray Goudie, Ian Townend and Dave Bankhead

338 Lord, we long to see your glory

Richard Lewis

339 Lord, you are more precious

Lynn DeShazo

340 Lord, you are so precious to me

Graham Kendrick

5 verses

Tenderly

341 Lord, you have my heart

Martin Smith

Tenderly

342 Lord, you put a tongue in my mouth

Ian Smale

3 verses

343 Love divine, all loves excelling (Tune 1)

John Stainer

8 verses

343a Love divine, all loves excelling (Tune 2)

William Penfro Rowlands

4 verses

344 Love of Christ, come now

Graham Kendrick

345 Low in the grave he lay

Robert Lowry

346 Majesty

Jack Hayford

347 Make a joyful noise, all ye people
(Worship the Lord)

Edwin Hawkins

348 Make me a channel of your peace

Sebastian Temple

3 verses

349 Make way, make way

Graham Kendrick

4 verses

350 Man of sorrows

Philipp Bliss

5 verses

351 May our worship be as fragrance
(A living sacrifice)

Chris Bowater

352 May the fragrance

Graham Kendrick

3 verses

Worshipfully

353 Meekness and majesty
(This is your God)

Graham Kendrick

3 verses

354 Men of faith
(Shout to the north)

(Martin Smith)

3 verses

355 Mercy is falling

David Ruis

356 Mighty God

Mark Johnson, Helen Johnson and Chris Bowater

2 verses

357 Mighty is our God

Eugene Greco, Gerrit Gustafson and Don Moen

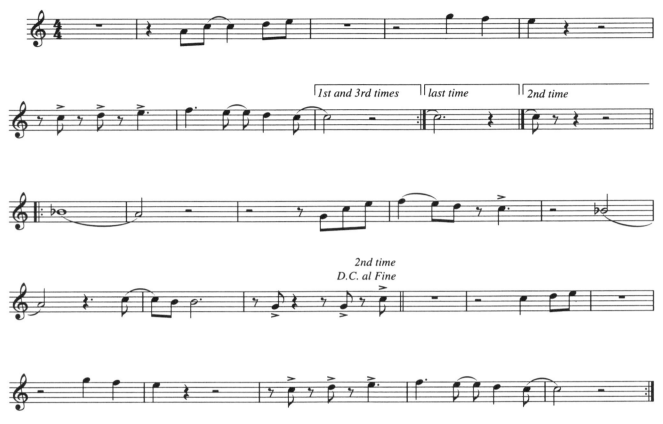

358 More about Jesus

J.R. Sweney

4 Verses

359 More love, more power

Jude del Hierro

360 More of your glory

Lindell Cooley and Bruce Haynes

361 More than oxygen

Brian Doerksen

3 verses

362 My first love
(Like a child)

Stuart Townend

3 verses

363 My heart is full
(All the glory)
Graham Kendrick

3 verses

Moderately
Verse

Chorus

364 My heart will sing to you
(Great love)
Robin Mark

2 verses

365 My hope is built (Version 1)
(The Solid Rock)
W.B. Bradbury

4 verses

With life

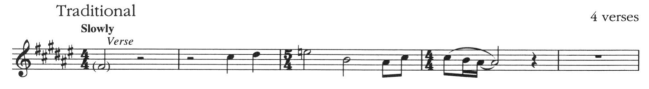

365a My hope is built (Version 2)
(The Solid Rock)
Traditional

4 verses

Slowly

366 My Jesus, I love thee

William R. Featherston and Adoniram J. Gordon

3 verses

367 My Jesus, my Saviour
(Shout to the Lord)

Darlene Zschech

Growing in strength

368 My life is in you, Lord

Daniel Gardner

last time to Coda

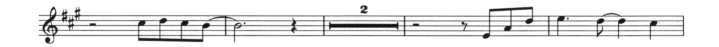

CODA

369 My lips shall praise you
(Restorer of my soul)

Noel and Tricia Richards

3 verses

With energy

370 My Lord, what love is this
(Amazing love)

Graham Kendrick

3 verses

With strength

371 My Spirit rests in you
(Shadow of your wings)

Reuben Morgan

2 verses

372 Nearer, my God, to thee

Lowell Mason

5 verses

373 No one but you, Lord
(Only you)

Andy Park

2 verses

Slowly, with strength

Verse

Chorus

374 No other name

Robert Gay

375 No scenes of stately majesty

Graham Kendrick

5 verses

376 Not by might

Robin Mark

377 Nothing shall seperate us

Noel and Tricia Richards

3 verses

378 Now unto the King
(Unto the King)

Joey Holder

379 O Breath of life

Mary Jan Hammond

4 verses

380 O come, all ye faithful

Possibly by John Francis Wade

6 verses

Verse

Chorus

381 O come and join the dance

Graham Kendrick

4 verses

(3rd verse instrumental)

Chorus

382 O Father of the fatherless
(Father me)

Graham Kendrick

4 verses

383 O for a thousand tongues to sing

Thomas Jarman

6 verses

384 O give thanks

Graham Kendrick

4 verses

Medium fast, reggae style

385 O God, most high
(You have broken the chains)

Jamie Owens-Collins

2 verses

386 O God of burning, cleansing flame

(Send the fire)

Lex Loizides

4 verses

387 O happy day

Ron Jones

4 verses

388 O, heaven is in my heart
(Heaven is in my heart)

Graham Kendrick

3 verses

389 Oh, I was made for this
(I was made for this)
Graham Kendrick

3 verses

390 Oh, lead me

Martin Smith

391 O Jesus, I have promised

Geoffrey Beaumont

5 verses

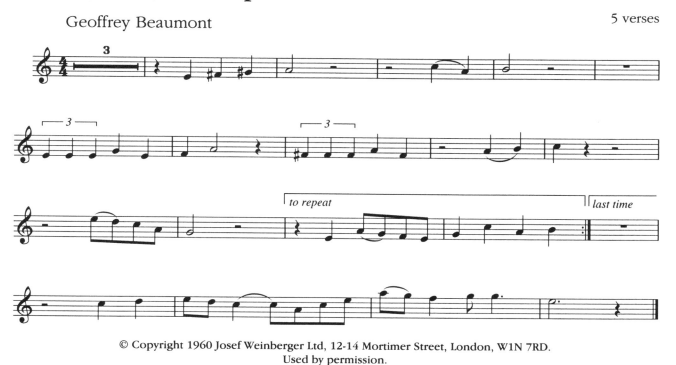

392 O let the Son of God enfold you
(Spirit song)

John Wimber

2 verses

393 O little town of Bethlehem

Traditional English melody collected by Ralph Vaughan Williams

4 verses

394 O Lord, hear my prayer

Jacques Berthier

395 O Lord, how majestic is your name
(How majestic)

Ben Lindquist and Don Moen

396 O Lord, my God
(How great thou art)

4 verses

Swedish folk melody collected by Stuart K. Hine

397 O Lord, my heart is not proud

Margaret Rizza

398 O Lord our God
(We will magnify)

Philip Lawson Johnson

3 verses

399 O Lord, the clouds are gathering

Graham Kendrick

With strength

4 verses

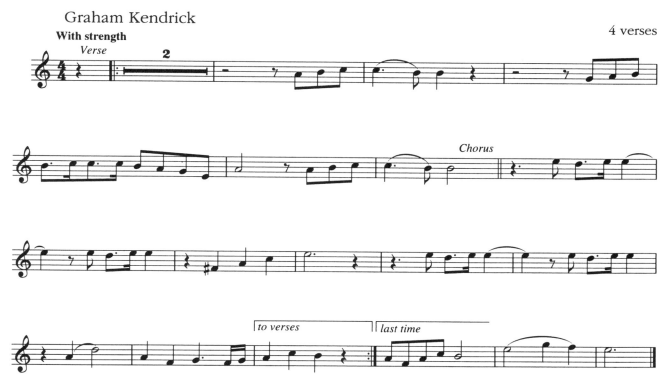

400 O Lord, you lead me
(Have faith in God)

Geoff Bullock

2 verses